14.95

Audition Son... ...r
Female Singers
R&B Anthems

Nine great songs ideal for auditions

Published by
Wise Publications
8/9 Frith Street,
London W1D 3JB, UK.

Exclusive Distributors:
Music Sales Limited
Distribution Centre, Newmarket Road,
Bury St Edmunds, Suffolk IP33 3YB, UK.
Music Sales Pty Limited
120 Rothschild Avenue,
Rosebery, NSW 2018,
Australia.

Order No. AM978340
ISBN 1-84449-217-6
This book © Copyright 2005 Wise Publications,
a division of Music Sales Limited.

Compiled by Nick Crispin.
Music arranged by Paul Honey.
Music processed by Paul Ewers Music Design.

CD recorded, mixed and mastered by John Rose & Jonas Persson.
Backing tracks arranged by Paul Honey.
Keyboards by Paul Honey.
Bass by Phil Mulford.
Drums by Chris Baron.
Backing vocals arranged by Cathryn Hopkins.
Backing vocals sung by Alison Symons & Paula Howard.

Printed in the United Kingdom by
Caligraving Limited, Thetford, Norfolk.

Your Guarantee of Quality
As publishers, we strive to produce every book
to the highest commercial standards.
The music has been freshly engraved and the book has been
carefully designed to minimise awkward page turns and
to make playing from it a real pleasure.
Particular care has been given to specifying acid-free,
neutral-sized paper made from pulps which have not been
elemental chlorine bleached. This pulp is from farmed sustainable
forests and was produced with special regard for the environment.
Throughout, the printing and binding have been planned to ensure a
sturdy, attractive publication which should give years of enjoyment.
If your copy fails to meet our high standards, please inform us and
we will gladly replace it.

www.musicsales.com

See page 64 for full CD track listing details

Wise Publications
part of The Music Sales Group
London/New York/Paris/Sydney/Copenhagen/Berlin/Madrid/Tokyo

CW00418278

1 Thing

Words & Music by Stanley Walden, Rick Harrison & Amerie Rogers

(Na na na na na oh,   na na na na na oh,   na na na na na oh,   na na na na na.)

1. Oh,   been tryin' to let___ it go,   tryin' to keep my eyes___ closed,
2. Hey! We don't know each oth - er well,   so why I   keep   picking up my cell?

Repeat and fade

Breathe

Words & Music by Charles Aznavour, Marshall Mathers, Ivan Matias, Melvin Bradford, Andrea Martin, Alvin Joiner, Richard Vick, Sean Henriques, Cantrell Blu, Stefan Harris, Richard Bembery & Gaby Wagenheim

Don't Cha

Words & Music by Thomas Callaway & Anthony Ray

that's why when-ev-er I come a-round___ she's all___ ov-er you.___
'cos if it ain't love___ it just ain't e-nough___ to leave a hap-py home.
I'd prob-ab-ly be___ just as cra-zy a-bout you if you were my old man.___

And I know you want___ it,   (I know you want___
Let's keep it friend-ly,   (Let's keep it friend-
May-be next life-time,   (May-be next life___

___ it.) it's ea-sy to see;   (It's ea-sy to see.)   and in the back___
- ly.) you'll have to play fair;   (You'll have to play fair.)   see, I don't___ care,___
___ time.) pos-sib-ly;___   (Pos-sib-ly.)   un-til then,___

Doo Wop (That Thing)

Words & Music by Lauryn Hill

1. It's been three weeks since you've been look-ing for your friend, the one you let it hit and nev-er called you a-gain.

Yeah, yeah.)__ - gain. Talk - ing out your neck, say -in' you're a Chris - tian. A Mus-lim sleep-ing with the gin. Now

'Mem - ber when he told you he was 'bout the Ben - ja - mins? You act like you ain't hear him but gave him a lit - tle trim. To be -

that was the sin that did Je - ze - bel in. Who you gon' tell when the re-per-cus-sions spin?

- gin, how you think you real - ly gon' pre-tend like you was-n't down, then you called him a - gain. Plus

Show-ing off your ass 'cos you're think-ing it's a trend, girl - friend. Let me break it down for you a-gain, you

1.

when you give it up so ea - sy you ain't ev - en fool-in' him. If you did it then, then you prob-'ly fuck a -

know I on - ly say it 'cos I'm tru - ly gen - u - ine: don't

look out, look out.___ 1, 3. Girls, you know you bet - ter___ watch out,___ some
2. Guys, you know you bet - ter___ watch out,___ 'cos

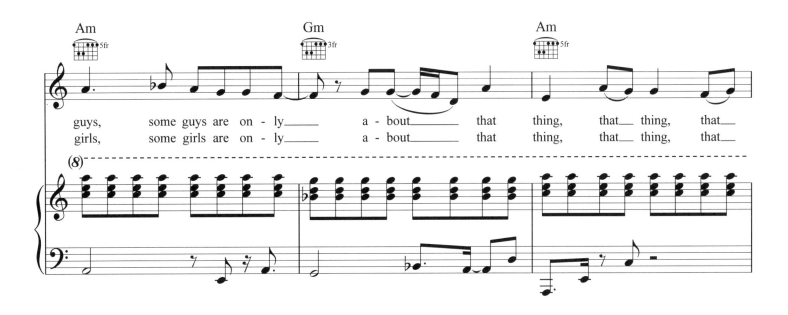

guys, some guys are on - ly___ a - bout___ that thing, that___ thing, that___
girls, some girls are on - ly___ a - bout___ that thing, that___ thing, that___

Play 3 times to fade

thing,___ that thing, that___ thing, that___ thing.
thing,___ that thing, that___ thing, that___ thing.

Milkshake

Words & Music by Pharrell Williams & Charles Hugo

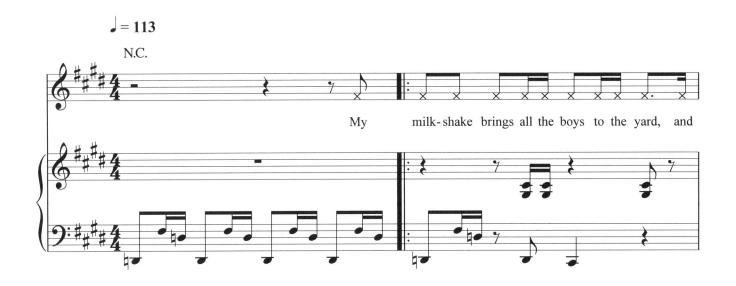

My milk-shake brings all the boys to the yard, and

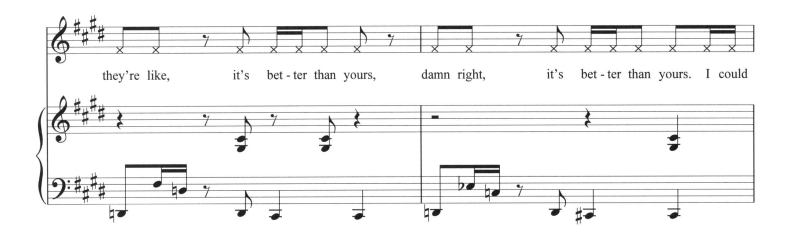

they're like, it's bet-ter than yours, damn right, it's bet-ter than yours. I could

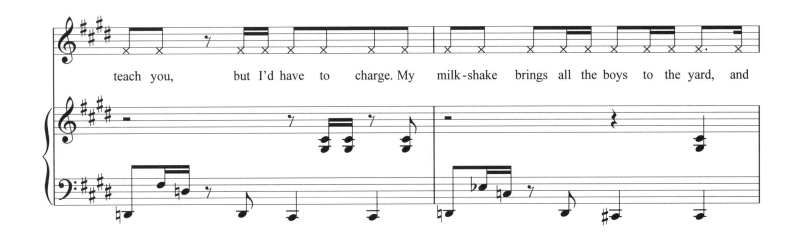

teach you, but I'd have to charge. My milk-shake brings all the boys to the yard, and

they're like,   it's bet-ter than yours,   damn right,   it's bet-ter than yours. I could

1. I know you   want it,   the thing   that   makes   me,
2. I can see you're on it,   you   want   me to teach the
teach you,   but I'd have to charge.

what the guys   go   cra - zy   for,___
tech-niques   that   freaks   these   boys,___

they lose their minds,   the way I whine,   I think it's   time.
it can't be bought,   just know thieves get caught,   watch if you're smart.

damn right, it's bet-ter than yours. I could teach you, but I'd have to charge. My

milk-shake brings all the boys to the yard, and they're like, it's bet-ter than yours,

damn right, it's bet-ter than yours. I could teach you, but I'd have to charge.

Bm   F#/A#   D   E5   Bm   F#/A#

Oh, once you get in-volved, ev-'ry-one will look this way so, you must main-tain your charm,

29

Real Love

Words & Music by Mark Rooney & Mark Morales

Say My Name

Words & Music by Rodney Jerkins, Fred Jerkins III, LaShawn Daniels, Beyoncé Knowles, LeToya Luckett, Kelendria Rowland & LaTavia Roberson

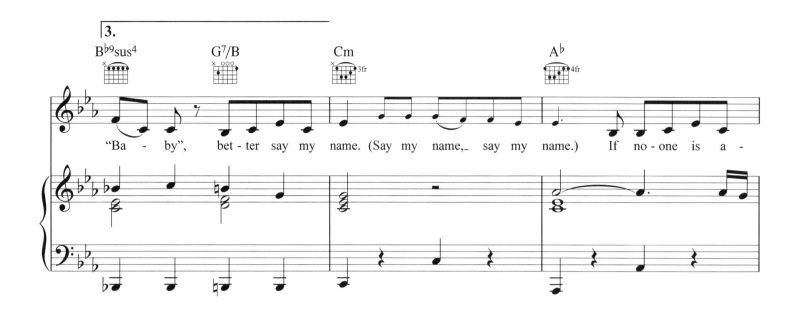

"Ba - by", bet - ter say my name. (Say my name,_ say my name.) If no - one is a -

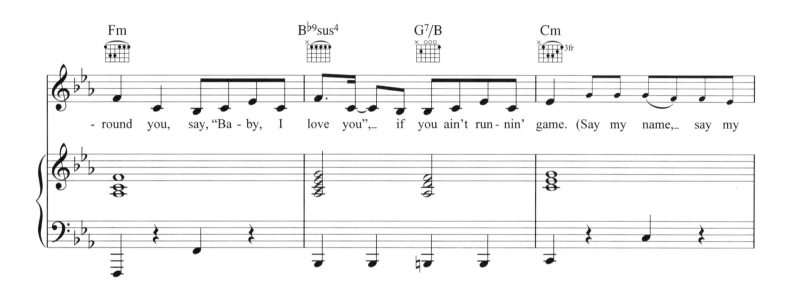

- round you, say, "Ba - by, I love you",_ if you ain't run - nin' game. (Say my name,_ say my

name.) You act - ing kind - a sha - dy ain't call - ing me "Ba - by", why the sud - den

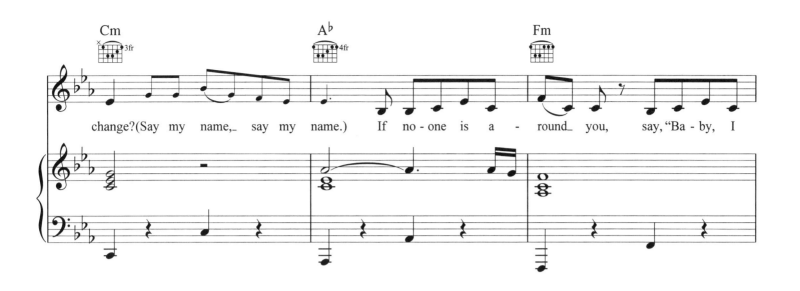

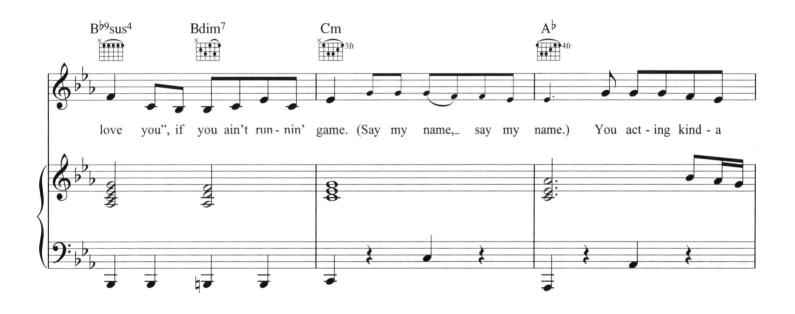

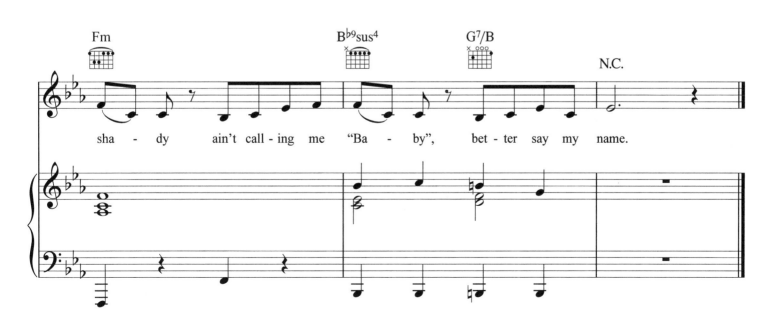

Superstar

Words & Music by Joseph Belmaati, Mich Hansen & Mikkel Sigvardt

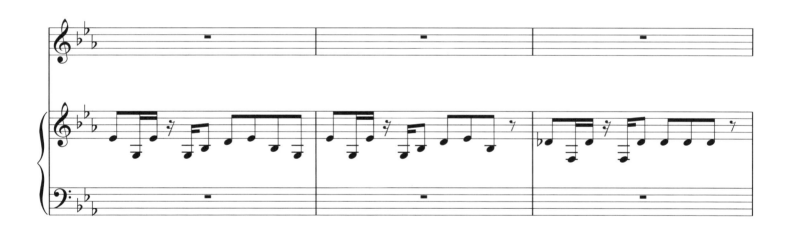

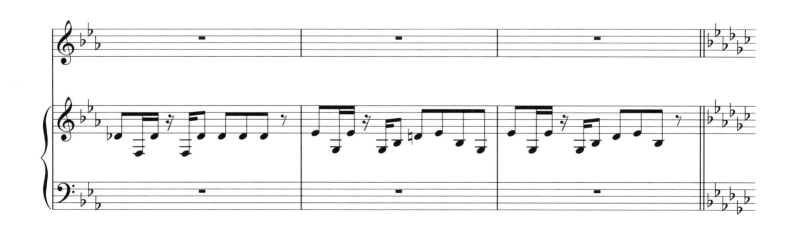

that makes me feel____ like this.____ Don't know...

D♭

Got to be, got to be____ a su-per-star.____

E♭m7

Oh, that's all you____ are.____

(You just make me wan-na play.)   (Lead vocal ad lib.)
(I don't know what it is____ that makes me

You Had Me

Words & Music by Francis White, Joss Stone, Betty Wright & W. Stoker

Tried to keep me down, I'm breaking free.
things you do and say em - bar - rass me. See,

I don't want no part in your next fix.
once up - on a time I was your fool, but the

Some - one needs to tell you this is it.
one I'll leave be - hind is you.

Hey, lis - ten, you'll be miss - in' out on my love and my kiss - in';

I don't want you here, mess-ing with my mind.

I've real-ised in time that my eyes are not blind.

I've seen it be-fore; I'm tak-ing back my life.

Am⁹   Bm⁷   C   D⁶   N.C.

You swore_ you had con-trol of it;___ when I___ stepped back,_ you slipped on your_ sup-ply.___

Em

B/D♯

Em

You had me,___ you lost me,___ you're wast-ed,___ you cost_ me.___

I don't want you here, mess-ing with my mind.

I've real-ised in time that my eyes are not blind.

I've seen it be-fore; I'm tak-ing back my life.

Tak-ing it back, I'm tak-ing it back, tak-ing back my life.

Taking it back, I'm taking it back, taking back my life.____ Ain't

no-bo-dy got____ no bus - 'ness____

stress-ing all___ the time.___ Tak-ing it back, I'm tak-ing it back,

tak-ing back___ my life.___

N.C.

1 2 3 4 5 6 7 8 9

CD Track Listing

CD Track 1
1 Thing
Music: Page 2
(WALDEN/HARRISON/ROGERS)
EMI UNITED PARTNERSHIP LIMITED/EMI MUSIC PUBLISHING LIMITED/COPYRIGHT CONTROL.

CD Track 2
Breathe
Music: Page 8
(AZNAVOUR/MATHERS/MATIAS/BRADFORD/MARTIN/JOINER/VICK/HENRIQUES/BLU/HARRIS/BEMBERY/WAGENHEIM)
SONY/ATV MUSIC PUBLISHING (UK) LIMITED/COPYRIGHT CONTROL/WARNER/CHAPPELL MUSIC LIMITED/EMI MUSIC PUBLISHING LIMITED/
MUSIC 1 LIMITED/NOTTING HILL MUSIC (UK) LIMITED

CD Track 3
Don't Cha
Music: Page 14
(CALLAWAY/RAY) NOTTING HILL MUSIC (UK) LIMITED

CD Track 4
Doo Wop (That Thing)
Music: Page 18
(HILL) SONY/ATV MUSIC PUBLISHING (UK) LIMITED

CD Track 5
Milkshake
Music: Page 26
(WILLIAMS/HUGO) BMG MUSIC LIMITED/EMI MUSIC PUBLISHING LIMITED

CD Track 6
Real Love
Music: Page 32
(ROONEY/MORALES)
RYKOMUSIC LIMITED/UNIVERSAL/MCA MUSIC LIMITED/STB MUSIC INCORPORATED

CD Track 7
Say My Name
Music: Page 40
(JERKINS/JERKINS III/DANIELS/KNOWLES/LUCKETT/ROWLAND/ROBERSON)
FAMOUS MUSIC CORPORATION/EMI MUSIC PUBLISHING LIMITED/SONY/ATV MUSIC PUBLISHING (UK) LIMITED

CD Track 8
Superstar
Music: Page 48
(BELMAATI/HANSEN/SIGVARDT)
UNIVERSAL MUSIC PUBLISHING LIMITED/WARNER/CHAPPELL MUSIC LIMITED

CD Track 9
You Had Me
Music: Page 56
(WHITE/STONE/WRIGHT/STOKER)
BMG MUSIC PUBLISHING LIMITED/UNIVERSAL MUSIC PUBLISHING LIMITED/COPYRIGHT CONTROL